How to Use Your *Story of Christmas* Book and Advent Calendar.

Set the Advent calendar up where all can enjoy it during the Christmas season. A mantelpiece or table might be a good place. Each day before Christmas, open one of the little pre-punched doors—on December 1st, door number 1, on December 2nd, door number 2, and so on.

When the door has been opened and the hidden picture revealed, turn to the correspondingly numbered episode in the book, and read the related story. There is one door and one story for each December night before Christmas. All combine to tell the story of the first Christmas in a unique and entertaining way.

The Advent calendar does not become obsolete like an ordinary calendar, so it and its accompanying book can be used year after year, becoming a happily anticipated part of a family's Christmas tradition.

The Story of Christmas

Concept created by
Kathryn Jackson

Story adapted by Kathryn Jackson

Illustrated by
Augie Napoli

gb **GOLDEN PRESS · NEW YORK**
Western Publishing Company, Inc., Racine, Wisconsin

 **1** Long ago—hundreds of years before that night of nights that was the first Christmas—a time of darkness and trouble lay upon the land and people of Judah.

There were long and cruel wars.

Wicked kings ruled over the people.

Rich landowners worked their servants long and hard, and paid them so little that they crept hungry to their cold beds.

Even the poor tore at one another like wild beasts, fighting for a crust of bread.

All men longed for the darkness to end.

Yet none knew how light might be returned to the dark and troubled world.

It was then that a good man—the Prophet Isaiah—called the people of Judah together so that he might bring them words of hope.

The people of Judah began to gather before the good and wise Prophet Isaiah.

Working men came from the vineyards and the close-cropped sheep pastures.

They came from the darkened, angry sea—where they had been casting nets and bringing in fish.

The women and children came from the poor, dark, little villages.

And there came also rich men, clad in fine garments, who stood well apart from the crowd.

Now when many people had come before him, the Prophet Isaiah begged them to look into their own hearts— from whence the darkness and cruelty had come.

"Be kind to one another," he said. "And walk in the way of God."

As the people listened, the Prophet Isaiah reminded them of a wondrous promise that had been made to all mankind a long, long time before.

"One day," he said, "a Child will be born to us, and He will be the Son of God and the Prince of Peace.

"He will bring love and peace into the world—and with these, the lost and longed-for light."

Now many listened in doubt to the words of the Prophet Isaiah.

"What says this greybeard?" they asked one another, and mocking him, they went their way.

But many believed his words, and waited in hope for the coming of the Child—the sweet Babe who had been promised to them.

At last, the time foretold by the Prophet Isaiah was at hand.

There lived in Nazareth at that time a young girl named Mary, who was soon to be wed to the carpenter Joseph.

Now Mary was as gentle as a white rose, so no darkness came near her— but only the joyful light.

One day, as Mary sat at her loom, an angel came down to her.

"Fear not, Mary," the angel said, "for you have been chosen — above all women—to bear the Son of God."

Mary wondered greatly at this, for she was a maiden not yet married.

Yet she bowed her head in obedience to the will of God.

And the angel departed from Mary.

Now also, in good time, a bright angel came to the carpentry shop of Joseph, Mary's betrothed husband.

Blinded by its light, he dropped his tools and fell at once upon his knees.

The angel, touching his head, said, "Lo, I bring tidings of great joy."

And having told of the Babe, whom they were to name Jesus, the bright angel departed also from Joseph.

Then Joseph went straightaway to Mary, that he might make her his wife.

Now neither Mary nor her husband Joseph told the townspeople of the wondrous tidings the angels had brought.

They kept the gladsome news in their own hearts until their God should make it known to all mankind.

6 As Mary waited for the day when the Babe would be born, she sat making soft swaddling clothes to wrap him in.

Joseph, waiting in his shop, made the things he sold to townspeople.

And as they waited, it seemed that all their town of Nazareth lay in a dream of quiet waiting, too.

The young leaves on grape vines and fig trees lay still on the soft waiting air.

Bees droned a slow waiting song.

And sheep, grazing on the hills, turned their ears as if listening for something that was to come.

Shepherds, leaning on their crooks and dreaming, asked, "Why do we wait?"

And husbandmen tending their crops also waited, not knowing why.

Still that air of strangely quiet waiting moved on, even to the broad Sea of Galilee that lay at the foot of the hills.

The water lay mirror-still, as it sometimes does before a storm.

"Lo, a great storm is coming!" cried some of the fishermen, drawing in their nets in sudden fear.

But others waited in hope, saying, "Nay, the time of great joy which was promised long ago is at hand."

Leaving their nets in the water, they sat down and broke their bread together.

And when, at the ending of the day, they drew in their nets—they had caught great numbers of fish.

These they shared with all who had need—even with the fishermen who had drawn in their nets in fear.

Now the air of hope and of waiting spread far off to the East—where lived the Magi.

The Magi were learned men who knew the prophecy of old.

But of them all, only three were awaiting the birth of the Babe.

These three were kings: Melchior, grown old with waiting; Caspar, who was of middle age; and also Balthazar, young king of the Moors.

Each, in his rich chamber, had his servants clothe him in garments fit for worshipping the Prince of Peace.

Each had his camel saddled and made ready for the journey—whether it be short or long—to see the Babe.

And each chose a gift for the Babe when at last He should come.

9 Melchior, clothed in royal purple, chose as his gift for the Babe a curiously worked cask of golden coins.

Caspar, robed in scarlet, chose a jeweled chalice of frankincense.

And Balthazar, resplendent in embroidered cloth of gold, chose a phial of precious oil of myrrh.

Now, in their palaces, the three kings studied the writings of scribes of old, seeking to find what sign would tell of the birth of the Babe.

And finding it written that there would be a bright star in the heavens, the Magi slept but little for a long and patient time.

Instead, each sat—chin on clasped hands—watching the heavens for the sign proclaiming the Babe's birth.

10 It happened in those days that the Emperor of Rome, ruler also of Judah, sent out a decree.

Trumpets sounded far and near, and messengers told all men to go to be taxed and counted, each in the city of his birth.

Joseph, who was of the house of the great King David, was to go to Bethlehem, the City of David.

He had planned to go alone, leaving Mary to await the Babe at home.

But Mary asked to go with Joseph.

"Let this be so," she said, "that the Babe may be born in Bethlehem, as was written long ago."

And Joseph listened to Mary and bowed to her wish.

He closed his small carpentry shop, and he and Mary made themselves ready for the journey to Bethlehem.

Early one morning, Mary and Joseph set forth for the city of Bethlehem.

Because Mary was heavy with child, Joseph wrapped her in a warm cloak, and set her upon a little donkey.

Rough roads and craggy mountains lay between Nazareth and the royal city of Bethlehem.

So they traveled for many days, with Mary riding and her husband Joseph walking beside her.

When Mary was thirsty, Joseph gave her cool water to drink.

When she was weary, he stopped to let her rest and sleep.

And all through the long journey, the little donkey trod carefully and gently, as if it knew of the Babe that lay close under Mary's heart.

So the long days passed.

When at last they came into Bethlehem, the City of David, Mary was weary from the journey.

And the hour for the Babe to be born was almost at hand.

But the city was crowded, for a great many people had come there to be taxed and counted.

Those who were rich had lodgings at the inns.

And those who were poor at least had friends or relatives with whom they could stay.

But Joseph, the humble carpenter from Nazareth, was a stranger in the city of Bethlehem.

He knew not where he and Mary—and the Babe who was soon to be born to her—would rest that night.

13 Leading the little donkey, Joseph went from house to house seeking shelter for the night.

The noisy crowds pushed by, shouting to one another and jostling Mary as she rode wearily through the strange and darkening city.

And at each house, the householder said, "There is no room here," and turned Joseph and Mary away.

In all the City of David, there was no room for the strangers.

No room for the tall, troubled man and his gentle wife, who was soon to give birth to a child.

Yet, as night and its chill fell upon Bethlehem, one innkeeper took pity on Mary and Joseph and offered them a resting place in his stable.

Now Joseph lifted Mary down from the little donkey and led her through the open door of the stable.

And lo, as she crossed the threshold, a vine grew up on the outer wall, blooming with one white rose.

As Joseph closed the door on the chill of the night, the sheep within the stable drew together to make room for the strangers.

So also the cows drew together.

The rooster, awakening, crowed as if to herald a new day.

Joseph knelt to prepare the manger as a crib for the Babe to come.

And Mary, having laid out the soft swaddling clothes she had made, lay down to rest and to await the wondrous birth which had been so long foretold.

15 As night wore on, certain shepherds waited on the hills, keeping watch over their sheep.

When they were overcome with sleep, one small shepherd boy stayed awake—watching the flocks, and the wide sky that cupped the hills.

And lo, in that night sky, a star of great size and brightness suddenly appeared. Higher and higher it climbed, stopping only when it blazed above the silent stable in Bethlehem.

There it shone with such great brilliance that the town, and hills, and fields glistened white—as if they were deep in new-fallen snow.

"It is the wondrous star!" the shepherd boy cried out in joy.

And he fell upon his knees.

16 One by one, the shepherds all awakened, rubbed their eyes, and wondered at the meaning of the bright star that shone above the stable.

And an angel appeared unto them, saying: "Fear not, for today I bring you tidings of great joy—which shall be to all men—

"For unto you is born in Bethlehem a Child who has come to save the world. You shall find Him wrapped in swaddling clothes, and sleeping in a manger."

Then suddenly, a host of angels appeared above the shepherds, praising God and saying:

"Glory to God in the highest,
and on Earth peace,
goodwill toward men."

17 The shepherds huddled in amazement until the angels had gone, leaving them alone on the hillside.

Then they arose, saying one to another:

"Let us go quickly down from the hills into Bethlehem, that we may see this Babe whom the angels have made known to us."

And they all went down in haste, even the one small shepherd boy who had watched through the night.

Taking a young lamb as a gift for the the Babe, he followed all the others.

And when they had come to the stable of the inn, the shepherds had the boy go first that he might lay his gift at the feet of the Babe.

 Far in the East, the Magi, those learned kings who had so long awaited this night of all nights, beheld the glorious star.

"The time of waiting is over," each thought with exceeding joy. "Here is the sign that the Babe is born—"

Each departed from his chamber.

And, taking up their gifts of gold, and frankincense, and myrrh, the Magi mounted their camels and rode afar— ever following the bright star.

First rode Melchior, in purple.

Next rode Caspar, in his scarlet.

And last rode Balthazar, in garments of gold, with his dark eyes fixed, too, upon the bright and glorious star that guided them on their journey from the East to Bethlehem, in Judah.

 As the Magi drew near to the city of Jerusalem, they were surrounded by a band of soldiers sent by King Herod to stop them.

The first two Magi were sore afraid.

"Stop us not!" cried Melchior.

"We ride in peace!" cried Caspar.

But Balthazar, dark eyes flashing, said boldly, "What does Herod the king want of us?"

"We ride in peace also," said the captain of the band. "Come, for the king wishes only to sup with you so that he may talk with you."

"We will come," said Balthazar.

And when he had spoken, Melchior and Caspar rode also with the soldiers, going in peace to the court of mighty Herod the king.

20 Now when the Magi came into the presence of Herod the king, he had a banquet set before them.

And when they had eaten, he asked them of their journey.

But having heard of the birth of the Babe—the Son of God and the Prince of Peace—King Herod lowered his eyes, to hide the evil in his heart.

"If this great Prince should grow to manhood," he thought, "He might wrest away my riches and power—"

Thinking so, Herod the king made up his mind that the Babe must die at the hands of his rough soldiers.

But to the Magi, he spoke honeyed words, saying: "When you have seen this Babe, come and tell me where He lies—so that I, too, may go forth and worship Him."

21 The Magi, having promised to do as King Herod asked, rode on.

And at last their journey came to an end.

Before them, in the silence of the night and under the glorious star, lay the stable in Bethlehem.

The Magi tethered their camels near a stream, so that they might refresh themselves after their long journey.

Then Melchior took his gift of gold from within his saddlebags.

Caspar took his gift of sweet-smelling frankincense.

And Balthazar took his gift of precious oil of myrrh.

Then the three kings, rejoicing in their hearts, formed a rich procession as they walked toward the stable to bow before the Babe who lay within.

When the Magi drew near to the stable, they saw that many others had come before them.

There were husbandmen, bringing grapes and figs as gifts.

And shepherds, bringing gifts of wool to be fashioned into garments for the newborn Babe.

Women came, with fresh bread they had baked for the strangers in the stable in Bethlehem.

And little children wandered about, plucking the flowers of the field to take to the sweet Babe.

For lo, the flowers of early spring— the red fire tulip, the white star-of-Bethlehem, and the fragrant pink—had suddenly put forth bloom.

Now when the people saw the Magi coming, they drew aside so that the three great kings might go first into the stable.

Melchior stepped forward.

And also Caspar.

But Balthazar, holding up his hand, asked them to wait so that those who had come before them might also enter the stable before them.

So it was that a poor beggar, shivering in his rags, went to the Babe before the noble Magi.

Many others followed after him.

And lo, all who went into the stable in darkness and sore trouble, came forth in brightness and joy because of what they had seen.

24

At last—with the light of wonder shining upon their faces—the Magi went into the stable.

And there they beheld a sweet, newborn Babe who was wrapped in swaddling clothes and sleeping in a manger.

Over Him leaned Mary and Joseph.

Round Him had gathered all the animals—the sheep and cows, and the little donkey—breathing upon Him to keep Him warm.

And all about the Babe there shone a tender and wondrous light such as no man had seen on Earth before.

"He has come, as was promised to us long ago," said Balthazar.

And Balthazar, Melchior, and Caspar bowed low before the Babe.

And from high above—just as on that night of nights that was the first Christmas—there came angel voices praising God, for the light had at last returned to the world.

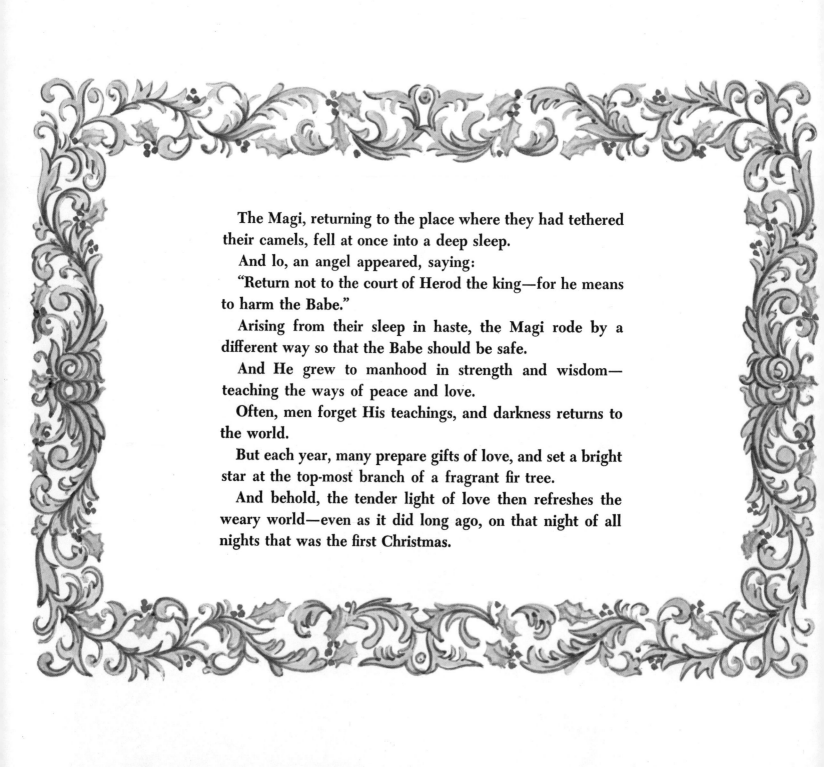

The Magi, returning to the place where they had tethered their camels, fell at once into a deep sleep.

And lo, an angel appeared, saying:

"Return not to the court of Herod the king—for he means to harm the Babe."

Arising from their sleep in haste, the Magi rode by a different way so that the Babe should be safe.

And He grew to manhood in strength and wisdom—teaching the ways of peace and love.

Often, men forget His teachings, and darkness returns to the world.

But each year, many prepare gifts of love, and set a bright star at the top-most branch of a fragrant fir tree.

And behold, the tender light of love then refreshes the weary world—even as it did long ago, on that night of all nights that was the first Christmas.